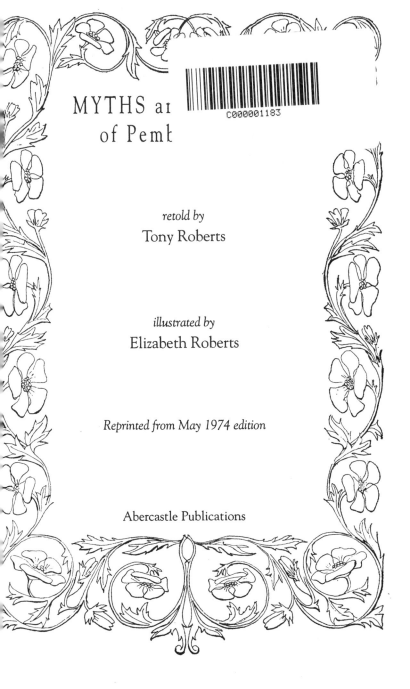

MYTHS and
of Pemb

retold by
Tony Roberts

illustrated by
Elizabeth Roberts

Reprinted from May 1974 edition

Abercastle Publications

i.   The Story of Pwyll, Prince of Dyfed

Pwyll went hunting from his chief palace at Narberth to Glyn Cuch. Losing his companions, he came across a stag hunted down by strange dogs glistening white with red ears and eyes. He drove them off and set his own dogs on, when up came a stranger clad in gray, on a gray horse. He reproved Pwyll, who handsomely apologised. The stranger was Arawn, King of Annwn, the Celtic Underworld. Pwyll agreed to do him a favour which was to spend a year in Annwn, looking like Arawn and living like him, and to kill his enemy Havgan. This had to be accomplished with only one stroke, for with more, he would recover. In return Arawn would rule Dyfed for a year. All this took place, and Dyfed prospered.

Then Pwyll courted the fair Rhiannon ; it was difficult at first since her white horse, though walking slowly, could not be overtaken at the fastest gallop. But at last, by the simple expedient of speaking to her, she stopped. At their betrothal feast though, Pwyll was asked a boon by Gwawl, which he thoughtlessly granted ; Gwal asked for Rhiannon, whom Pwyll then had to give up, a year hence. But Rhiannon, after telling Pwyll off, got over this by producing a magic bag which Gwawl was induced to get into. It was then tied up, and Gwawl got a beating . . . "and then was the game of Badger in the Bag first played."

Then the nobles of Dyfed came to Pwyll at Preselau and grumbled that he had no heir, and wanted him to take another wife. Pwyll asked for another year, and a little boy was born. But he disappeared the night he was born. Rhiannon's servants, afraid they would be blamed and killed for this, blamed her and charged her with devouring the child. Rhiannon had to do penance.

The little boy suddenly appeared in the house of Teirnyon, Lord of Gwent Iscoed, who had a fine mare which foaled on the 1st May always ; unfortunately the foal always disappeared. One night, she was brought into the house to foal so Teirnyon could watch ; when the mare foaled, a huge claw came through the window to take the colt. Teirnyon cut off the claw with his sword and dashed out in the direction of the noise and wailing that followed. He found nothing but when he came back, there was a baby boy. Eventually he heard about Rhiannon's trouble, and recognised the boy as Pwyll's son. So he took the child back.

The boy was called Pryderi and he ruled Dyfed after Pwyll.

ii. *Manawyddan*

Prideri married Kicva and suggested to his friend Manawyddan, who had nothing to do, that he run his kingdom of Dyfed, and marry his mother Rhiannon into the bargain "when she was in her prime none was ever fairer. Even now her aspect is not uncomely."

This all went through well, and all four feasted at Narberth and took their ease and hunted. Then one day came a tremendous thunderstorm and a thick mist enveloped everything. When it cleared, the land was deserted, all human beings and animals had disappeared, and only the four of them remained.

They lived a couple of years by hunting and on wild honey, then they went to England to earn a living. They worked in Hereford at making saddles, and did it so well that the local craftsmen became jealous and would have killed them ; so they went on to another city and made shields. But the same thing happened, and they went to a third city where they made shoes. When they were chased out here, they decided to go back to Dyfed.

At Narberth they hunted for a year and then one day they chased a pure white boar which disappeared into a castle which was strange to them, though of course they knew the district well. They were afraid to go in, but wanting to get his hounds back, Prideri ventured inside, and picked up a golden dish in a marble fountain. And there he stuck. Manawyddan didn't dare go in and in the evening he went

3

back to Narberth where he was soundly berated by Rhiannon for deserting Prideri. So she went herself to rescue him and she also stuck. So Manawyddan and Kicva only were left, and they went back to England and made shoes for a living. But they were driven out again by the jealous cordwainers. Back they came to Dyfed but this time Manawyddan brought some wheat back and sowed it at Narberth. A wonderful crop grew.

But when he came to reap the first field, he found every single ear gone. And this happened to a second field. So he lay in wait in the third field the night before reaping. With a loud rustling noise a huge army of mice came and started eating the corn. He chased them but managed to catch only one, slower than the rest, put it in his glove, and took it back to Narberth, determined to hang it the next day as punishment.

Kicva tried to dissuade him, but he was firm. Then, as he was about to hang it, a scholar appeared and tried to dissuade him too, offering to buy it off him. He refused, and then a priest came up and tried too. Again he refused and again as he was about to hang the mouse, a whole bishop's retinue came up. The bishop offered him much more but still he refused.

"What would you take ? asked the bishop.

"Give me back Prideri and Rhiannon," he said.

The bishop agreed, but Manawyddan also wanted the charm taken off the whole county of Dyfed; to which he also agreed.

"Tell me, who is the mouse ?"

"She is my wife. I am Llwyd of Kilcoed and I came to avange the insult paid to Gwawl. Llwyd waved a wand over the mouse who changed into a lovely woman ; and Dyfed was re-peopled, then the corn waved in the wind, the cattle lowed and the sheep bleated, as before. And nobody, except the four, knew that anything had happened.

iii. *Kilhwch and Olwen*

Kilhwch was the son of a prince and, though he had never seen her, he fell in love with Olwen, daughter of the savage giant, Yspaddaden Penkawr.

"Go to Arthur your cousin," said his father, "and ask him to cut your hair and help you."

Arthur cheerfully offered the assistance of all his knights and they set out to achieve the seemingly impossible tasks set by the giant, at which everyone hitherto had failed.

They had to grub up a hill, plough, sow and ripen the grain in a day, find the missing Mabon lost in infancy, hunt the Twrch Trwyth and perform numerous other tasks, and if successful, the giant would die.

Mabon was found by asking the oldest creatures, blackbird, stag, eagle, owl and salmon, the other tasks accomplished by magical help and the hunt for Twrch Trwyth begins.

The mysterious Twrch Trwyth was a monstrous boar, with seven young pigs, transformed for his sins from a King into a swine. Between his ears he had a comb, razor and scissors which Arthur had to take as one of the impossible tasks.

So Arthur went to Ireland to ask for the comb etc., but the Twrch was so angry at being transformed to a swine that he wouldn't speak to Arthur, let alone yield comb, razor and scissors. What was more, he took the battle into Arthur's country. With his seven young pigs, he landed at Porth Clais. Arthur and his men, horses and dogs went to Mynyw (St. David's), missing Twrch whom he overtook after the pigs had killed all they found of men and beasts along Abergleddyf (Milford Haven).

Arthur followed Twrch Trwyth as far as Preselau and Twrch made a stand along the Nevern. From there he went to Cwm Cerwyn and slew four of Arthur's champions ; and made a second stand and slew four more, and was wounded himself. The next morning before day, he killed four more and, with these, many men of the country.

Then Arthur pursued him to around Llandissilio and he killed four more before going on up to Cardiganshire ; all over South Wales they chased the boar and pigs, losing many men. Eventually only Twrch himself was left and in the Severn estuary, they seized the scissors and razor but he escaped to Cornwall where they managed to get the comb. But Twrch swam out to sea and was seen no more.

Kilhwch and Arthur's men went to the giant and cut off his head and Olwen became Kilhwch's wife.

CANTRE'R GWAELOD

The Cantre'r Gwaelod, or Bottom Hundred, was a great tract of fertile country extending from Ramsey Island north to Bardsey Island over what is now Cardigan Bay. It was 40 miles long and 20 wide, low and level, highly populated and cultivated, with 16 fortified towns "better than all the towns of the Cymry except Caerleon-on-Usk." The King was called Lord of Cantre'r Gwaelod in Dyfed (i.e. Pembrokeshire), although most of the land lay closest to what is now Cardiganshire. It was defended from the sea by a strong embankment and sluices.

The Lord of the Cantre'r Gwaelod in 520 A.D. was Gwyddno Garanhir ; and the Keeper of the Embankment was Seithennin, "one of the three immortal drunkards of Britain."

One evening there was a great banquet and Seithennin, in his usual state, left the sluices open. The sea came in remorselessly and the land was inundated. Those of the inhabitants who were not drowned escaped to Ardudwy, part of Caernarvon, and ascended the mountains of Snowdonia, the first time they had been populated.

Nowadays when the sea is very still and the water clear, the walls and buildings are said to be seen still, and when the water below moves them, the church bells sound faintly.

༺༻༺༻༺༻༺༻

THE GREEN ISLES OF THE SEA

A century ago, so the tradition says, sailors on the coast of Pembrokeshire had actually landed on islands out at sea where the Plant Rhys Ddwfn, children of Rhys the Deep, lived. This was the name given in West Wales to the Fair Folk, the Tylwyth Teg, or, if you like, Fairies. The curious thing was that when the sailors returned to their boats, the islands simply vanished from view.

But the Fair Folk were well known : they used to come to local markets regularly at Haverfordwest, Milford, Laugharne, Cardigan and Fishguard. They were seen sometimes by a few sharp-sighted people, but their presence was known by many.

"Oh, they were here today," people used to say to each other on their way back from market when prices had been high and everything sold. Without speaking they bought their meat, corn and other necessities, putting down silver pennies as if knowing what they would have been charged. The farmers liked them because they bought corn well, but the poorer labourers resented their forcing up prices.

Gruffydd ab Einon was in St. David's churchyard one day when he suddenly saw the islands out at sea. He went to put out to sea at once but the islands had disappeared ; a second time, too, the same thing occurred. The third time, though, he took with him the turf on which he had been standing, and he landed on the islands safely. He was warmly welcomed by the little people and shown their many treasures, for they were great traders.

"How do you manage to stay here in safety ?" he asked one shrewd little old man, before leaving.

"There are strange herbs that grow here and nowhere else, so that the islands cannot be seen. Only here do they grow and on the turf in St. David's churchyard ; and also on one square yard on one place in Cemmaes."

"But how can you be sure that one of you won't betray the secret of the herbs ?" persisted Gruffydd.

"Oh," said the little man, "that is due to the teaching of Rhys, patriarch of our people. He told us to honour our parents and ancestors ; to love our wives without looking at those of our neighbours and to do our best for our children. We do that, and no-one is unfaithful to another. A traitor is a wholly imaginary character among us : we see him with a head like the Devil, and ass's feet, and hands like a man's, holding a large knife and the family dead around him."

Gruffydd continued to be a friend of the children of Rhys and became very wealthy, but after his death relations between the Rhysians and farmers in Cardigan became strained because the farmers put the prices too high and the Rhysians took offence. The old people thought they then went to Fishguard as very strange people had been seen there, and it was, after all, before the days of tourists.

ELIDORUS AT ST. DAVID'S

When Elidorus was a boy of 12 in Dewisland (the St. David's Peninsula) he ran away from school to avoid the strict discipline and frequent canings. He hid in a river bank where he found a hollow ; after a couple of days he was getting pretty hungry and wondering what to do about it, when two little men came up to him and invited him to a country "full of delights and sports". He followed them with alacrity through a dark path and then out into a most attractive countryside with rivers, meadows, woods and fields.

He was taken to the king who questioned him at length and then handed him over to his son, who was about the same age as Elidorus. They played together, and Elidorus learned quite a bit of the language.

He often went back to his own world ; sometimes by the way he had first come, and sometimes by a different way.

He described the little people to his mother at great length. They were very small, he said, but well built, with a fair complexion and long hair over their shoulders like women. They had small horses and greyhounds. They lived on a milk diet, made up "into messes" with saffron, but they ate no meat or fish. They never took an oath and detested lies. They had no form of public worship, being devoted only to truth and each time they came back from our upper world, presumably from the markets, they couldn't stop talking about our infidelities, inconstancy and ambition.

But Elidorus's mother spoilt it : she wanted a present and he had told her they often played with golden balls, so she told him to bring one back for her.

And so he did, but he was followed by two little men, and in his haste, he stumbled just as he reached home. They pounced on him, seized the ball and derided him contemptuously as they ran back. Terribly upset that they should feel like that about him because of his mother, he tried to go back and explain but, try as he would, he could never find the passage by the river bank.

He got over it at last, and went on to train for, and eventually, become a priest ; when questioned late in life by the Bishop of St. David's, David II, Elidorus told him the story.

THE MERMAID AT ABERBACH

It was in the early part of last century when, one fine morning early, the farmer at Treseissyllt went down to the sea at Aberbach. Aberbach is a small and lovely beach at the end of a tiny, and now, wild valley. It has a fine big shingle bank thrown up at the mouth of the valley ; and sand and rocks at low water. The cliffs on either side are wild and dangerous, especially on the north where the large farm of Treseissyllt, large for North Pembrokeshire, that is, extends to the cliff edge.

It was low water and as the farmer came down to where the lime kiln is, he stopped suddenly. For, stranded inside the shingle bank by the retreating tide, was a young and beautiful mermaid. Mermaids are always described as beautiful ; and this one really was, we are told. Perhaps it is only the rather vain and beautiful ones who spent so much time by the shore and on the rocks doing their hair, which seems to have been their main pre-occupation, who got caught by retreating tides.

Anyway, without more ado, the farmer picked her up, thrashing about wildly, and carried her up the path to the farm where he put her in a tub, which he filled with salt water. She pleaded tearfully for him to let her go, but he only chuckled.

"Oh, no," he said, "I've got other ideas for you." At this, she became really alarmed. Finally, in a rage, she put a curse on the farm that no child would be born there again ; and then the farmer, rather alarmed, did take her back again and put her in the sea.

For over a hundred years, the curse hung over the heads of the farmers of Treseissyllt.

And yet . . . there was some compensation. "Duw, duw," said one old farmer, who was leaving, to his successor, "You're a lucky man."

"Why ?" asked the younger man, surprised.

"Well, you won't be able to get the servant girls into trouble, will you ?"

One fine September afternoon at the beginning of the eighteenth century, a fisherman from St. Dogmael's named Pergrin, or Peregrine, was fishing near Cemaes Head. Thinking he saw some movement, he went silently inshore towards a recess in the cliffs, and there on a rock, he saw a mermaid combing her hair. Quietly but carefully he came alongside and, jumping out, seized her and carried her back on board, struggling wildly and threshing about with her tail. But Peregrine had got her securely and she could not get away.

We do not know what language mermaids speak normally, but this one spoke fluent Welsh and between her tears she begged Peregrine to let her go. But it is not every day that one finds a mermaid and he was most reluctant, although he was rather distressed to see how upset she was. Then, with a last effort, she said, "Peregrine, if you will let me go, I will give three shouts to you in your hour of greatest need." So Peregrine released her, thinking he would never really see her again. And for weeks he did not. Then one hot afternoon, when the sea was calm and Peregrine and a number of other fishermen were out fishing, he suddenly saw the head and shoulders of the mermaid appear in the sea by his boat.

"Peregrine ! Peregrine ! Peregrine !" she cried urgently, "Take up your nets ! Take up your nets !

Peregrine was surprised for the afternoon was fine, and the sea showed no sign of any danger. But he instantly pulled in his nets with haste and back he went, past the bar and no sooner was he in than a terrible storm broke out. Eighteen others who had gone out were all drowned.

🎔🎔🎔🎔🎔🎔

THE CUCKOO OF NEVERN

In Nevern churchyard is the famous Celtic Cross similar to that at Carew, only, as Fenton says, more elegantly wrought. On this cross on 7 April, the patronal day of the parish, the cuckoo is supposed to sing for the first time in the year. One year, the priest and congregation were waiting expectantly but the bird was late. Eventually it did come and feebly started to sing—then fell dead from exhaustion. The second tree in the churchyard in that fine line of yews, is supposed to weep till a Welshman shall again rule in the castle up the hill.

WITCHCRAFT AT MATHRY

At Mathry there was a celebrated witch whom people believed was guilty of often bewitching cattle. One day, when a servant girl of a farm in the neighbourhood went out to milk in the morning, she found all the cows in a sitting position "like cats before a fire." And whatever she did, she could not get them to move. The farmer suspected the witch so he went and made her come with him.

When she came, she said there was nothing wrong with the cows and she simply put her hand on the back of each animal and it immediately got up.

ST. EDREN'S CHURCHYARD

The ancient well in the churchyard of St. Edren's (B4330 from Haverfordwest to Croesgoch, as far as Newton Cross and straight on) was a holy well. It cured madness but the ritual attached to it no longer exists.

According to tradition, the well dried up because of pollution : a woman washed clothes in it on a Sunday. Another tradition was that a farmer brought a mad dog to drink out of it, whereupon the farmer died but the dog recovered. Anyway, the virtue of the water was miraculously transferred to the grass growing round the base of the church walls, called porfa'r cynddeiriog, the grass of the mad. It was a cure for hydrophobia, and eaten as a sandwich between bread. A money offering was put in a stone trough in the church wall.

A Gwiber (flying snake) is said to have flown from St. Edren's church tower to near Grinston where it lives in marshy ground, at night time coiling up in the bottom of Grinston well. But it can hardly have flown from the present church which is entirely Victorian.

THE TOADS OF TRELLYFFANT

A curious story is told of the farm called Trellyffant near Nevern. If you go on the coast road from Newport to Moylegrove for about 4 miles, the farm lies down to the right and there is a fine prehistoric burial chamber in a field just visible from the road.

But the story, as told by Giraldus Cambrensis, relates how a young man, Cecil Longlegs, "during a severe illness, suffered as violent a persecution from toads, as if the reptiles of the whole province had come to him by agreement ; and though destroyed by his nurses and friends, they increased again on all sides in infinite numbers, like hydras' heads. His attendants, both friends and strangers, being wearied out, he was drawn up in a kind of bag into a high tree, stripped of its leaves ; nor was he there secure from his venomous enemies, for they crept up the tree in great numbers, and consumed him to the very bones."

CILGERRAN : THE BEAVERS OF THE TEIFI

The river on which Cilgerran stands is the Teifi, justly famous for its salmon, the finest in Wales, as Giraldus Cambrensis said even before 1200. But in Giraldus's day there were also beavers on the Teifi, the only river in England and Wales still to have them. Giraldus pays tribute to the skill of beavers building their fortifications in the middle of rivers with the "appearance of a grove of willow trees, wide and natural without, but artfully constructed within."

But, continues Giraldus, without a hint of irony, "when the beaver finds that he cannot save himself from the pursuit of the dogs that follow him, that he may ransom his body by the sacrifice of a part, he throws away that which by natural instinct he knows to be the object sought for, and, in the sight of the hunter, castrates himself ; and if by chance dogs should chase an animal which had previously been castrated he has the sagacity to run to an elevated spot, and there lifting up his leg, shows the hunter that the object of his pursuit is gone. And to corroborate his account of natural history, Giraldus quotes Juvenal and St. Bernard.

THE BOY ON THE FRENI FAWR

One day, a boy of about twelve or so was looking after his father's sheep on the Freni Fach, not far from Crymych. The scene then must have been a little different from what it is nowadays—less fencing and no forestry, but the little Welsh mountain sheep in the clear June sunshine looked much the same. And there is now a metalled road round the foot of the Freni Fawr, the bigger hill, under a mile away. These hills are great stretches of moorland and pasture at the eastern end of the Presely mountains.

When he got to the pasture, there was still a little mist on the mountain top and he looked over to the Freni Fawr to see which way the mist was going. The people in those parts always said that if the mist went down on the Pembrokeshire side, the weather would be fine, but if it went down on the Cardigan side, it would be bad.

As he looked round the still and tranquil scene, he suddenly started with surprise, for over on the Freni Fawr was a party of what looked like soldiers, busily occupied. "No," he said to himself, since he knew the ways of the military, "Soldiers wouldn't be out so early in the day. Anyway, they're too small for soldiers." So he walked further up the hillside and to his surprise, they really were Tylwyth Teg or the Fair Folk ; or, as some called them, the Dynion Bach, the Little People ; and they were dancing.

He knew all about them of course, everyone did, and he had often seen their rings, but he had never seen them before. He thought of running home to tell his parents, but decided against it because there was every chance the Fairies would be gone by the time he got back,

So he decided to go nearer to get a better view, and anyway he didn't think the Little People would hurt him. He edged nearer and soon he was unobtrusively stationed quite close to the ring, and he stayed there some time watching. As he described them later, they were of both sexes, extremely handsome and very cheerful. They were not all dancing, but those who did stayed carefully to the circle. Some of the ladies were riding on small white horses. All were elegantly dressed in different colours—it was the red coats which had made him think at first they were soldiers.

After a while they saw him and made signs for him to join in ; and as he put one foot in the ring, he heard the most beautiful and irresistible music. Almost immediately he found himself somehow in an elegant palace. Here he was liberally entertained, accompanied by beautiful girls, and offered mouth-watering foods, instead of the usual "Tatws a Llaeth" (potatoes and buttermilk), and wine in abundance, brought in golden glasses. One restriction only was laid on him : he was not under any circumstances, to drink from a well in the middle of the garden. He solemnly agreed not to and the round of pleasure went on.

Then, one day, an innate curiosity got the better of him, and he plunged his hand in the forbidden well. The fishes instantly disappeared, a confused shriek rang through the hall and garden. Instantly the palace disappeared and he found himself back on the hillside and the sheep peacefully grazing as he had left them (sheep unlike cows are not responsive to the Little People).

Sadly he looked round the hillside for any signs of the Little People or the ring or castle. But, of course, there were none.

THE BRYNBERIAN MONSTER'S GRAVE

As you approach the village of Brynberian just off the B4329 from Cardigan to Haverfordwest over the mountain, the Preseli Mountains lie on your left. About a quarter of a mile on your left, across the moor is the Bedd yr Avanc (the monster's grave). The Welsh word Avanc means Beaver, but it also has a more horrifying significance, a water monster. There are other Welsh folk tales of the afanc, sometimes huge and hairy, able to take human form, even at times a dwarf or a water-horse similar to the Scottish water-horse and kelpie.

But little seems to be known of the Brynberian afanc except that he was caught in a pool near Brynberian Bridge and taken up and buried on the mountain-side.

There may not be an avanc there at all. The archeologists say this is a Neolithic gallery grave dating from about 2500 B.C. and with an outer parallel row of stones on each side similar to those of southern Ireland.

※ ※ ※ ※ ※ ※

WITCHCRAFT IN THE GWAUN VALLEY

During the early part of last century, and later, the Gwaun Valley was reputedly full of witches, especially of the descendants of one particular old woman. One well-known family who practised the black art wanted to become members of Caersalem Baptist Chapel, and were admitted. But it made no difference to their behaviour.

One witch, even on the day she became a communicant, bewitched a young servant girl of Gelli Fawr farm. She was sitting in a pew behind the girl who rushed out of the chapel and ran wildly about the roads. Her father, having tried every means of pacifying her, went to Cwrt-y-Cadno to consult Dr. Harries, the famous Carmarthenshire wise man. Dr. Harries told the father what had happened and even showed him the scene in a mirror. He gave him a piece of paper with some words written on it which the girl had to wear on her breast. And this was quite sufficient to bring her back to a normal condition.

On 22nd February 1797, an unseasonably hot Wednesday, a retired sailor, John Williams who farmed Treleddyn, St. David's, watched four men-of-war passing St. David's Head. Though they wore British colours, he recognised them as French. Sounding the alarm, he followed them on the coast.

The ships entered Fishguard Bay at 2 p.m. The fort at Pen Parc fired—though they had only three rounds—and the ships tacked back round Pen Caer, anchored and landed troops and stores at Carreg Gwasted, an exceedingly difficult task up a steep cliff. But it was accomplished by the early hours of Thursday, and the Second Black Legion, some 1400 Grenadiers and military convicts under an elderly American, Tate (who spoke no French), was ready to start the career of terror and destruction laid down in their orders.

The first thing they did was to loot the farms on Pencaer, eat ravenously, calves, sheep and poultry, "geese boiled in butter", and get so drunk on brandy and wine that many were ill for weeks. Pickets were posted at Garn Gelli and Garnwnda.

There was no body of professional soldiers to oppose them. Colonel Knox marched the Fishguard Militia in the direction of Haverfordwest as fast as he could, hastening past the side roads lest he be seen by the French.

The Lord Lieutenant, Lord Milford, promptly handed over command to Squire Campbell of Stackpole, newly created Lord Cawdor, who had studied military tactics, but who had never heard a shot fired in anger. He mustered some 500 assorted men to oppose the French and stationed them on the hill before Goodwick Sands. The country people with home-made weapons and some 400 Welsh women with their red cloaks and tall hats crowded the hills too.

The frigates sailed away at noon on Thursday, and Tate with his drunken troops was left to advance on the British. The bad shape of the Legion was emphasised by their threatening to shoot their officers in response to an order of Tate's to punish one man.

By 10 p.m. on Thursday, the French force offered to

capitulate without firing a shot, and on Friday this was confirmed. The Invasion was over.

The news of the surrender spread : "it was a grand sight" said an eye-witness, "to look on the surrounding hills crowded with innumerable spectators of both sexes ; the women, in their scarlet mantles and round hats, appeared at a distance like so many soldiers."

At 2 o'clock on Friday, the Frenchmen, drums beating and colours flying, laid down their arms on Goodwick Sands, crying, "To the devil with the Republic," and flinging down their tricolour cockades when Lord Cawdor told them to think no more of the Government that had abandoned them.

The invasion was over but the legend of the Welsh women lived on, and in particular that of Jemima Nicholas, "a tall, stout Amazon masculine woman who worked as a cobbler in Fishguard. Imbued with the noble and patriotic spirit of the old Cambria, she took a pitch-fork and boldly marched to Pencaer to meet the invading foe. On her approach she saw in a field about twelve Frenchmen. Not a whit daunted she advanced to them and whether alarmed by her courage or persuaded by her rhetoric, she had the address to conduct them to the guard-house at Fishguard."

WAKE NIGHT IN THE GWAUN VALLEY

An uncanny event took place at a Gwylnos (Wake-night) at Dolgaranog in North Pembrokeshire towards the end of the eighteenth century. A notoriously ungodly old gentleman farmer had died and was laid out in his coffin. The candles were lit and the people came to the house. Wake Night went on as usual, according to the custom. Some of the lads and girls were making rather merry when there suddenly came a sound of horses' galloping, approaching the house. The next moment the sound of men's footsteps was heard ; the door opened and footsteps crossed the room where the wake night was being held ; nothing was seen. But as they passed through, the invisible intruders put out the candles. Their presence could even be felt, but everyone was far too frightened to do anything. Then the footsteps left as they had come, the visitors re-lit the candles, the clatter of horses could be heard leaving and it gradually died away.

When the alarmed relatives and friends went into the room where the coffin was, to see what had happened, there was nothing but an empty coffin ; for the corpse was gone and it never was found. The coffin was afterwards filled with stones and buried.

THE VISION AT MORFIL

In 1853 Mr. John Meyler of Cilciffeth was walking home from Morfil one night. The prehistoric Flemings Way crosses the present day B4313 here ; on the left looms Mynydd Cilciffeth and to the right, as you come from Morvil are the Preseli Hills proper, Foel Eryr first. Even nowadays, all round are lonely, brooding expanses of moorland.

When Mr. Meyler neared Penterwin, about a third of his way home he aws the image of armies in the sky. There were several batallions at first, but then they increased till they went right across the sky. There were two opposing forces discernible and he could distincly see men falling and horses galloping across the heavens.

He was so terrified that he called at Penbanc and Mr. James Morris, who lived there, went out and saw the same thing. The whole phenomenon lasted about two hours.

THE GHOSTLY VISITOR AT CASTLEBYTHE

Castlebythe is a lonely and remote hamlet consisting of a few farmhouses only, in the northwest of the county and near Castlebythe Mountain, a huge expanse of high and lonely moorland. Even now it is little visited by strangers, and at the turn of the century, with poorer roads and no cars, it was distinctly less so.

One night, when the family were seated by the simne fawr (the great chimney) in the farmhouse, the silence was broken by a voice. It appeared to come from outside the little window near the skew (settle) by the fire, a piece of furniture you can still find, and which then was seen in all Welsh kitchens.

Everyone froze, mostly in surprise but also with an uneasy feeling of fear. Then the silence was broken again by the sound of rattling which came from the little shed outside. Someone rushed out to see ; in an extraordinary way, the big end-over-end butter churn was turning, apparently by itself, with a large stone inside it, which could only with difficulty be got out.

The whole affair happened again, and yet again ; the knowledge of it spread around, and neighbours, the bolder ones at least, came in to hear it : just the voice, though nobody could distinguish the words, and the sound of the churn ; nothing more. At last, some of the men decided to go outside and wait, hiding in big old trees in the haggard, with a shotgun to loose off at anything they saw.

The next night, the voice came but they saw nothing, either at the window, or by the churn. So the following night they tried again, and there seemed to be a movement, so they let fly with both barrels. The trees all seemed to light up mysteriously, but that was all.

They came back in, but then the farmer seemed to sense something that strangely no-one had noticed before. The one person unaffected by the happenings was Maire, the servant girl sitting quietly knitting in the corner. He ordered her brusquely away; and, curiously enough, that was the end of the strange voice and churning.

THE WISE MAN OF NORTH PEMBROKESHIRE

There was at one time an unusual sort of man called a "Dyn Hysbys", with undoubtedly psychic powers. Such a man could cure sickness of both body and mind, and could foretell the future. Some attained quite a remarkable degree of fame.

One of the most famous, well beyond his native county, was Dr. Harries, popularly known as Abe Biddle, of Werndew. His name was a household word around the Fishguard area, and much further afield, in the early part of the nineteenth century. There are many stories of his mastery of the occult. In the winter of 1803 there was an evening party at a vicarage in North Pembrokeshire. The company consisted of clergymen and their guests but it was a gay evening, lasting until the early hours, with singing, tale-telling and merry-making.

The conversation drifted round to the occult in a desultory way until an elderly cleric, in no uncertain terms, denounced all sorcery and witchcraft ; the other clergymen gravely agreed nodding assent.

Biddle said nothing, although invited to speak, for he was after all well known for his powers.

During a lull, he rose suddenly, then disappeared through the French doors on to the lawn. He came back very shortly holding three small rings. He held them up. "Now, gentlemen," he said quietly, "we'll see what is possible." He placed them on the floor, then quickly left the room, locking the door on the outside while everyone's gaze was fixed on the rings. Suddenly in one of the rings, a fly appeared, buzzing. It grew and grew and turned into a huge hornet ; it flitted into another ring and was replaced in the first ring by another fly which also turned into a hornet. The guests became uneasy and then alarmed as more and more hornets came and droned loudly around the room. Then more and more came, darkening the ceiling, getting in people's hair and fighting everybody. Amid the confusion and shouting, Biddle opened the door and the hornets wheeled out and the droning grew fainter until it disappeared. The party was spoiled but there was no more scornful denunciation of powers beyond the scope of normal people.

A PHANTOM FUNERAL IN THE GWAUN VALLEY

Together with the Corpse Candle, the Toili or Phantom Funeral was the most prominent death portent in Pembrokeshire. This Gwaun Valley story dates from this century.

A young man who worked as a porter on the G.W.R. near Cardiff came home ill. A friend of his sat up with him all night. About three in the morning, the friend was so worried that he went for the patient's father, an elderly man living in a cottage near by.

As he went outside, he found, to his astonishment, that he was in a large crowd of people, and there was a coffin resting on some chairs, ready to be placed on the bier. The whole scene was a funeral procession ready to take the dead to the cemetary. When the young friend tried to go on his way, the procession also went on, so he found himself in the crowd still. After a hundred yards or so, he managed to extricate himself and reached the cottage of the patient's father.

Three days later, the young porter died, and his friend noticed uneasily that the crowd and coffin were exactly the same as he had seen three nights before.

☒☒☒☒☒☒

THE LEGEND OF ROCH CASTLE

The gaunt tower of Roch Castle, rising from a mass of volcanic rock, is a landmark for many miles around St. Bride's Bay. This is the furthest north that the Normans pushed on the west coast of Pembrokeshire and the castle marks the boundary line between Welsh in the north and English to the south.

In the 13th century, the feudal Norman Lord, Adam de la Roche, had a premonition that he would die from an adder's sting. But he would not have to fear after a year had passed in safety. So he built the castle and ensconced himself in the top storey. The year passed, and, with only a few days to go, everyone was rejoicing. But the wind blew across St. Bride's Bay and the wintry weather was bitterly cold. A servant brought in some firewood so the Lord of Roch could warm himself. He did so, but when he fell asleep before the embers, an adder crept from the remaining faggots of wood and stung him. In the morning, they found him dead.

THE TREFGARN PROPHECY

In the late eighteenth century, a farmer named Thomas Evans lived on a small farm named Penyfeidr, near Trefgarn Rocks. Both Mr. Evans and his wife Sarah, were renowned for their piety. Mrs. Evans, a Bevan from Martel Mill, was renowned possibly more for her ability to foresee future events.

Coming into the house one day, she said she had just seen a most remarkable sight in Trefgarn Valley below the house. She described it as a large number of heavily laden carts or wagons going very fast one after another, but with no bullock or horse pulling them ; but the first one appeared, from the smoke she saw, to be on fire.

This was some fifty years before George Stephenson first introduced steam locomotive power. About 1850 the railway was brought to Pembrokeshire. The famous engineer Isambard Brunel intended to extend it northward towards Fishguard and cuttings were made in Trefgarn Valley so it was thought the prophecy would be fulfilled.

But Brunel abandoned the scheme and took the line to New Milford (now Neyland) instead. So strangely the prophecy seemed to be contradicted. And even when the branch line was later made, it was miles to the north of Trefgarn, so once again the old lady's prophecy was ridiculed.

But then it was found later by the G.W.R. that the old loop line via Letterston was not suitable for a fast direct service to London so it was finally decided to make a new line from Goodwick through Trefgarn Valley, Brunel's original idea, as foreseen by Mrs. Sarah Evans, and this is where the line now runs.

THE WISTON BASILISK

Long ago there were several claimants to the estate of Wiston, Castell Gwys, near Haverfordwest, which was founded by Wizo, the Flemish Lord of Dungleddy (Daugleddau), the area between the Western and Eastern Cleddau rivers.

A basilisk lived in a hide on Wiston Bank nearby, much feared by everyone ; and rightly so, for the basilisk, though quite small—about a foot or two long, was a fabulous monster, a reptile with a black and yellow skin, death-dealing breath and eyes in the back of its head as well as the front and the ability to kill by its baleful gaze. The only compensation was that if a human being saw the basilisk without being seen, the monster would die.

It was agreed that anyone who could look at the basilisk without being seen should inherit the estate. This seemed quite reasonable as anyone who was first seen by the monster would not live to inherit anyway. Several claimants tried unsuccessfully, until one thought of an idea. He took a barrel to the top of the hill and got inside. Then he let it roll down the hill past the spot where the serpent lived. As he passed he looked through the bung and called out, "Ha, bold basilisk. I can see you but you can't see me." In this way, he became owner of the Wiston estates.

A WITCH AT WALTON WEST

A well-known old witch was coming home from Haverfordwest Fair one day in a cart with a farmer who had kindly taken her As they were driving along the road between Haverfordwest. and Walton West, they saw three teams harrowing in a field.

"Could you stop those teams by spells ?" asked the farmer.

"I could stop two of them," said the witch, "but the third teamster has a piece of mountain ash fast to his whip so I cannot do anything to him."

SIR RHYS AND THE KING AT DALE

When the Earl of Richmond was about to land in Wales from France, Sir Rhys ap Thomas consulted a noted wise man in Dale to find whether the Earl would be successful in his bid to dethrone King Richard III. The wise man was reluctant to prognosticate but finally he did produce a cryptic rhyme :

"Full well I wend, that in the end
Richmond, sprung from British race,
From out this land, the boare shall chase".

Henry VII, as the Earl of Richmond later became at Bosworth, needed some re-assurance too, after the landing, and he also went to a wise man Dafydd Llwyd, a bard and prophet. He was in doubt as well, but in his case it was resolved by his wife who advised him to prophesy in favour of Henry, if since the latter failed, Llwyd would hear no more about it, but if Henry won it would make his fortune.

Henry VII, the first Welsh king of England, landed from Brittany on 1 August 1485 at Mill Bay near St. Ann's Head.

His arrival placed Sir Rhys, the great potentate of south-west Wales, ' little less than a prince,' in something of a moral quandary. He supported Henry strongly as a loyal Welshman, but he had given an oath of allegiance to Richard III, that he would permit no landing except over his body. Advised by the Bishop of St. David's that this was not binding, he brought his 8000 men to march with Henry but took the precaution of lying beneath Mullock Bridge to let the future Henry VII walk over his body

❧❧❧❧❧❧

ST. BRIDE'S CHAPEL

In the little bay of St. Bride's was once a great herring fishery ; and just above the beach was once a small chapel where the fisherman used to pray both for success and that they might avoid the perils of the sea. According to Fenton,* the stone coffins projecting to-day from the earth eroded by the sea at high water are those of fishermen. The chapel fell into disuse

*the Pembrokeshire historian.

24

and there is a tradition that out of the ruins of the chapel a salting house was made for the fish ; but from that day the herrings failed.

"When St. Bride's Chapel a salt-house was made
St. Bride's lost the herring trade".

THE WATER HORSE OF ST. BRIDE'S BAY

The Ceffyl Dwr, or Water Horse, was one of the most firmly believed spectres in rural Wales in the past. It was generally a small but beautiful horse which tempted unwary travellers to ride but suddenly galloped away throwing the rider to destruction, except ministers who were allowed a peaceful journey.

The Water Horse was often seen on the shore, dappled, grey or like the sand in colour. One was seen in St. Bride's Bay after a storm. A farmer caught it and harnessed it to the plough. Everything went well for some weeks. Then, apparently seized with an impulse, the Water Horse dragged both plough and ploughman through the field at a furious pace, down to the shore and into the sea, disappearing in the waves.

A DEATH OMEN IN ST. BRIDE'S BAY

The Tolaeth was a sound heard before a death. It was a rapping or knocking ; sometimes thuds or shuffling. It was very widespread all over Wales and many people living today can vouch for it. Carpenters, for example, or their families, have heard knocking in the workshop as of their making a coffin—before a death.

A fisherman living on the shores of St. Bride's Bay was disturbed for three successive nights by sounds downstairs of shuffling feet, doors opening and the noise as if men were carrying a burden and putting it down. His wife heard the same noises and they heard them only in the kitchen. Both were frightened because this could only be the Tolaeth.

A few weeks later their son was drowned and his body was brought home on a ladder. To their horror the sounds were reproduced exactly : the shuffling of feet, moving of chairs and the grunting sound of the men setting down their burden.

A little south of Llawhaden is St. Kenox, once known as the Chancellor's House. In it lived the Reverend Rhys Pritchard when he was Chancellor of St. David's in 1620.

In his youth at Oxford he was more inclined to drinking than studying for the Church, and when appointed Vicar of Llandovery, he was notorious for his drunkenness. He spent most of his time in taverns.

He had a large goat which he sometimes took with him and one day, out drinking, he offered it some ale. The goat liked the taste and both Vicar and goat drank till they were hopelessly intoxicated. The next time he went drinking, the goat went too, but when he offered it ale again, the animal recoiled in disgust. This affected the Vicar as nothing had done before.

"How much wiser than I am," he said to himself, "this poor animal can profit where I cannot."

And from that day on, he reformed and touched not a drop of drink again.

More than that, henceforth, the Vicar became a great preacher of the Gospel in West Wales. And he also wrote poems which were gathered together as "Canwyll y Cymry", the Welshman's Candle, and which have made his name live for over three hundred years.

A GHOSTLY SHIP'S VISITOR

Captain Alldridge, R.N., assumed command of H.M.S. Asp as a surveying vessel in 1850. As he took over, the Dockyard Superindendant said :

"Do you know that this ship is haunted ? I don't know if you will get any of the Dockyard men to work in her." Alldridge smiled and pooh-poohed the idea, but before a week was out, the shipwrights came to him in a body and asked him to give up the ship as she would bring nothing but bad luck. Such an idea was clearly anathema to the Captain and eventually the repairs were finished.

But there were some queer happenings, as the Captain himself admitted. As he sat in his cabin in the evenings reading, either alone or with an officer, there were often noises, bangings and clatterings in the empty after cabin. This was next to his cabin and was always empty ; it was, too, unreachable from the ship except by the companion ladder leading to both cabins ; the Captain, from his cabin, could see anyone going to the after cabin.

Once, at Queensferry, the Captain was returning on board one night and he thought from the noise coming from his own cabin, that he had caught the ghost there. But quickly though he rushed in, there was nothing to be seen.

One night, shortly after, the quartermaster burst in saying the look-out had reported the figure of a woman standing on the paddle-box and pointing Heavenwards. The look-out man went into convulsions on being ordered back to his post, and the Captain crossly had to spend the rest of the night on look-out himself.

When the ship was lying at Lawrenny in the Cleddau one Sunday afternoon, the steward was spoken to by an unknown voice, and was so terrified that the captain reluctantly granted him a discharge. And the ship's work came near to being disrupted by the number of sailors who wanted a discharge and who deserted when it was not granted. The Captain himself was made of sterner stuff, but even he confessed to his hair standing on end when a hand was placed on his forehead at night ; though he came to take for granted the opening of drawers and banging of his wash-stand top.

Finally in 1857, the vessel put into Pembroke for repairs. On the first night in harbour, the dockyard sentry reported that a woman's figure mounted the paddle box, pointing upwards, and then came ashore towards him. He challenged her but she walked through his musket, which he dropped as he bolted for the guard-house. The next sentry saw all this and fired at the apparition. A third sentry saw the figure mount a grave in the old Pater Churchyard and vanish. All the sentries were so scared that the guard had to be doubled (as the Guard Report Book verified). The ghost was not seen again.

The only explanation the Captain could later offer was that before being commissioned, the Asp had been an Irish packet boat. After one trip, the stewardess found the body of a beautiful girl in a cabin with her throat cut. Nothing about her was ever discovered.

THE ORIELTON POLTERGEIST

Giraldus Cambrensis, in the Itinerary through Wales, relates how an "unclean spirit" appeared in the house of Stephen Wiriet ; the date would be about 1190. The spirit manifested itself by throwing dirt "more with a view of mockery than of injury."

"The spirit in a more extraordinary manner conversed with men, and, in reply to their taunts, upbraided them openly with everything that they had done from their birth, and which they were not willing should be heard or known by others. I do not presume to assign the cause of this event, except that it is said to be the presage of a sudden change from poverty to riches, or from affluence to poverty and distress ; as it was found to be the case. And it appears to me extraordinary that this place could not be purified from such illusions either by the sprinkling of holy water, or by the assistance of any other religious ceremony ; for the priests themselves, though protected by the crucifix, or the holy water on devoutly entering the house, were equally subject to the same insults."

ST. GOVAN'S CHAPEL

Close to Bosherston, that most attractive and unspoilt village (provided the Army is not allowed to extend the tank range at Castlemartin), is St. Govan's Chapel. To get there, you go straight on from Bosherston until you get to the coast, and there, halfway down the cliff steps, is St. Govan's chapel and well.

The Ancient Monuments Commission Report says cautiously that the chapel "may" be of 13th century construction, but St. Govan himself is unknown. He may have been but a generation or two ago people had no doubt but that he was Sir Gawaine ; yet one more Arthurian figure linked with the county.

The pamphlet obtainable in the church gives a different origin for St. Govan.

The rock and well were protected by supernatural power. Gawaine was hidden here by enchantment according to one story ; escaping from pirates, says another. The rock opened letting him into a vertical cleft, then closed again, protecting him from his enemies. When they had gone, it opened again and it remains open, leaving the impressions of his body. If anyone wishes in the cleft before turning round to come out, his wish will be fulfilled. The steps are said to be uncountable by mortals—different up and down (are there 52 ?), and whatever hopes are in one's mind when going up and down, if breathed lightly on the wind, will be granted. Below are magic stones, which ring like bells when touched. In the arch above the chapel, a bell hung for centuries and often sounded without human aid. It was said that the sound of a bell was a death or a disaster at sea.

Just below the chapel under a stone hood is the holy well, and until this century it was visited by people with eye ailments and rhumatism. Earth from fissures round the chapel was sprinkled round farm and homestead to avert evil.

🌣🌣🌣🌣🌣

OTHER BOSHERSTON LEGENDS

Another curious legend attached to St. Govan's : a farmer was sowing barley on Trevalen Down above St. Govan's, when he noticed a dignified, striking-looking stranger watching. The farmer approached him and in reply to the stranger's question, "What are you doing ?" replied that he was "sowing barley." "But," said the stranger, "this seed you are putting into the ground will decay."

"Yes," said the farmer, "and it will spring again and at harvest time I shall gather it."

"Do you believe," asked the stranger, "that that which is dead can come to life ?"

"I do," said the farmer.

"Then, go home," said the stranger quietly, "and get thy sickle and cut thy corn. For I am the Resurrection and the Life." The farmer did so, and on his return, the stranger had disappeared but the barley was ripe for harvesting the same day it had been sown.

Nearby on the cliffs is the Huntsman's Leap, where a lone rider leaped the chasm. Perhaps he died of fright on looking back, or perhaps he only accomplished the feat because his horse was blessed and he thus escaped losing the soul he had sold to the devil. Bosherston Mere was frequented by apparitions and myserious moans and wailings.

> There is nothing to hope and nothing to fear
> When the wind sounds low on Bosherston Mere
> There is much fear and little to hope
> When unseen hands pull St. Gowan's rope ;
> And the magic stones, as the wise know well,
> Promise sorrow and death, like St. Gowan's bell.

The handsome farm buildings on the cross-roads leading to Bosherston are Sampson Farm which has one of three celebrated standing stones. The others are at Stackpole Farm and on Stackpole Warren and are said to meet annually "to dance the hay at Sais's (Saxon's) Ford, and then, the dance over, to resume their station."

It was said to be very good luck to see the dance, but on the other hand the devil played his flute and witches held their revels there.

A PHANTOM FUNERAL AT PENALLY

In the south of the county, the phantom funeral was known as a "fetch funeral," and this account of one dates from mid-Victorian times.

A man working for the Vicar of Penally told him that on the previous evening he had met a large funeral procession near Holloway Farm, naming several neighbours among the mourners. The Vicar gently ridiculed the idea.

"But," said the man, " curious thing was that they carried the coffin over a bank."

"Then surely," said the Vicar, "You can show me the place, since the hedge will be all trampled down."

The man pointed out a place in a narrow lane near Holloway Farm, assuring the Vicar that that was where the procession left the road and passed into a field. But when they looked there were no signs of any passage through the hedge.

Shortly after, Mr. Williams, the tenant of Holloway, died and as a snowdrift blocked the lane, the coffin was taken over the bank on the way to Penally cemetary.

There is a tradition that St. David himself prayed that the people should have some sign to prepare themselves for death ; and that there should also be a sign to the living of the reality of another world. In a vision he was told that the Welsh and apparently more particularly those in the St. David's diocese, would have some forewarning of when and where death might be expected. This takes the form of a Canwyll Corph, or Corpse Candle, and it is seen passing along the route of a funeral, or hovering round the spot the dead person would be, or where an accident would happen.

This particular story relates to a young school mistress lodging near Tenby in a farm house.

One night she was lying awake when she saw a light like a little star moving towards her bed from the doorway. The light came to a standstill by her bed and lowered itself to her feet.

Terrified, she screamed and all the members of the household came running to find out what had happened, and then to comfort her.

Nothing more happened and some six weeks later she went off on holiday. While she was away, the farmer's wife, a strong healthy woman was suddenly taken ill and quite unexpectedly died. The young schoolmistress was told and hurried back for the funeral. When she arrived and was taken upstairs she found that the body had been laid out in the spare bedroom she herself had occupied and where the light had appeared.